Health and Safety
Commission

Management of Health and

C000142571

Management of Health and Safety at

Approved Code of Practice

L21

London: HMSO

ISBN 0 11 886330 4

Enquiries regarding this or any other HSE
publications should be made to the HSE
Information Centre at the following address:

HSE Information Centre
Broad Lane
Sheffield
S3 7HQ
Tel: (0742) 892345
Fax: (0742) 892333

This Code gives guidance on the application of the Management of Health and Safety at Work Regulations 1992 in all work activities to which the Regulations apply, including construction. It is expected that new regulations on construction site management will be developed to implement the Temporary and Mobile Construction Sites Directive, which was adopted on 24 June 1992. When the new regulations are made, it is envisaged that they will be accompanied by a new Approved Code giving guidance on the new construction regulations and supplementing this Approved Code of Practice on the application of the Management of Health and Safety at Work Regulations 1992 to construction. Those concerned with the management of health and safety in the construction industry will therefore need to read both Approved Codes of Practice and it is intended that both Codes will be published in one document for that purpose.

Contents

Notice of Approval *vi*

Preface *vii*

Introduction *1*

Regulation 1 Citation, commencement and interpretation *1*

Regulation 2 Disapplication of these Regulations *2*

Regulation 3 Risk assessment *2*
General principles of risk assessment *2*
Purpose of risk assessment in this Regulation *3*
Suitable and sufficient *3*
Review and revision *4*
Risk assessment in practice *4*
Assessment under other Regulations *7*
Recording *7*
Preventive and protective measures *8*

Regulation 4 Health and safety arrangements *9*

Regulation 5 Health surveillance *9*

Regulation 6 Health and safety assistance *10*

Regulation 7 Procedures for serious and imminent danger and for
danger areas *13*
Danger areas *14*

Regulation 8 Information for employees *15*

Regulation 9 Co-operation and co-ordination *16*
Appointment of health and safety co-ordinator *17*
Persons in control *17*

Regulation 10 Persons working in host employers' or self-employed
persons' undertakings *18*

Regulation 11 Capabilities and training *19*
Training *20*
Refresher training *20*
Adaptation/working hours *21*

Regulation 12 Employees' duties *21*

Regulation 13 Temporary workers *22*
Fixed-duration contracts *22*
Employment businesses *23*
Self-employed *23*

Regulation 14 Exemption certificates *23*

Regulation 15 Exclusion of civil liability *24*

Regulation 16 Extension outside Great Britain *24*

Regulation 17 Modification of instrument *24*

The Schedule *25*

By virtue of Section 16(1) of the Health and Safety at Work etc. Act 1974 ('the 1974 Act') and with the consent of the Secretary of State for Employment, the Health and Safety Commission has on 3 September 1992 approved the Code of Practice entitled *Management of Health and Safety at Work*.

The Code of Practice provides practical guidance with respect to the provisions of the Management of Health and Safety at Work Regulations and Sections 2, 3 and 4 of the 1974 Act.

The Code of Practice comes into effect on 1 January 1993.

Signed

T A GATES
Secretary to the Health and Safety Commission

4 September 1992

This Code of Practice has been approved by the Health and Safety Commission, with the consent of the Secretary of State, under section 16 of the Health and Safety at Work etc Act 1974 for the purpose of providing practical guidance with respect to the provisions of the Management of Health and Safety at Work Regulations 1992 and Sections 2, 3 and 4 of the 1974 Act.

Although failure to comply with any provision of this Code is not in itself an offence, that failure may be taken by a Court in criminal proceedings as proof that a person has contravened the regulation or sections of the 1974 Act to which the provision relates. In such a case, however, it will be open to that person to satisfy a Court that he or she has complied with the regulation or section in some other way.

1   The duties of the Management of Health and Safety at Work Regulations, because of their wide ranging general nature, overlap with many existing regulations. Where duties overlap, compliance with the duty in the more specific regulation will normally be sufficient to comply with the corresponding duty in the Management of Health and Safety at Work Regulations. For example, the Control of Substances Hazardous to Health Regulations (COSHH) require employers and the self-employed to assess the risks arising from exposure to substances hazardous to health. An assessment made for the purposes of the COSHH Regulations will not need to be repeated for the purposes of the Management of Health and Safety at Work Regulations. Other instances where overlap may occur include the appointment of personnel to carry out specific tasks or arrangements for emergencies. However, where the duties in the Management of Health and Safety at Work Regulations go beyond those in the more specific regulations, additional measures will be needed to comply fully with the Management of Health and Safety at Work Regulations.

2   Words or expressions which are defined in the Management of Health and Safety at Work Regulations or in the 1974 Act have the same meaning in this Code unless the context requires otherwise.

Citation, commencement and interpretation

(1)   These Regulations may be cited as the Management of Health and Safety at Work Regulations 1992 and shall come into force on 1st January 1993.

(2)   In these Regulations -

"the assessment" means, in the case of an employer, the assessment made by him in accordance with regulation 3(1) and changed by him where necessary in accordance with regulation 3(3); and, in the case of a self-employed person, the assessment made by him in accordance with regulation 3(2) and changed by him where necessary in accordance with regulation 3(3);

"employment business" means a business (whether or not carried on with a view to profit and whether or not carried on in conjunction with any other business) which supplies persons (other than seafarers) who are employed in it to work for and under the control of other persons in any capacity;

"fixed-term contract of employment" means a contract of employment for a specific term which is fixed in advance or which can be ascertained in advance by reference to some relevant circumstance; and

"the preventive and protective measures" means the measures which have been identified by the employer or by the self-employed person in consequence of the assessment as the measures he needs to take to comply with the requirements and prohibitions imposed upon him by or under the relevant statutory provisions.

(3)   Any reference in these Regulations to -

(a)   a numbered regulation is a reference to the regulation in these Regulations so numbered; or

(b)   a numbered paragraph is a reference to the paragraph so numbered in the regulation in which the reference appears.

Disapplication of these Regulations

These Regulations shall not apply to or in relation to the master or crew of a sea-going ship or to the employer of such persons in respect of the normal ship-board activities of a ship's crew under the direction of the master.

Risk assessment

(1)   Every employer shall make a suitable and sufficient assessment of -

(a)   the risks to the health and safety of his employees to which they are exposed whilst they are at work; and

(b)   the risks to the health and safety of persons not in his employment arising out of or in connection with the conduct by him of his undertaking,

for the purpose of identifying the measures he needs to take to comply with the requirements and prohibitions imposed upon him by or under the relevant statutory provisions.

(2)   Every self-employed person shall make a suitable and sufficient assessment of -

(a)   the risks to his own health and safety to which he is exposed whilst he is at work; and

(b)   the risks to the health and safety of persons not in his employment arising out of or in connection with the conduct by him of his undertaking,

for the purpose of identifying the measures he needs to take to comply with the requirements and prohibitions imposed upon him by or under the relevant statutory provisions.

(3)   Any assessment such as is referred to in paragraph (1) or (2) shall be reviewed by the employer or self-employed person who made it if -

(a)   there is reason to suspect that it is no longer valid; or

(b)   there has been a significant change in the matters to which it relates;

and where as a result of any such review changes to an assessment are required, the employer or self-employed person concerned shall make them.

(4)   Where the employer employs five or more employees, he shall record -

(a)   the significant findings of the assessment; and

(b)   any group of his employees identified by it as being especially at risk.

General principles of risk assessment

3   This Regulation requires all employers and self-employed persons to assess the risks to workers and any others who may be affected by their undertaking. Employers with five or more employees must also record the significant findings of that assessment.

4   Many employers already carry out *de facto* risk assessments on a day-to-day basis during the course of their work; they will note changes in working practice, they will recognise faults as they develop and they will take necessary corrective actions. This Regulation however requires that employers should undertake a systematic general examination of their work activity and that they should record the significant findings of that risk assessment.

5   A risk assessment should usually involve identifying the hazards present in any undertaking (whether arising from work activities or from other factors, eg the layout of the premises) and then evaluating the extent of the risks involved, taking into account whatever precautions are already being taken. In this Approved Code:

(a)   a hazard is something with the potential to cause harm (this can include substances or machines, methods of work and other aspects of work organisation);

(b)   risk expresses the likelihood that the harm from a particular hazard is realised;

(c)   the extent of the risk covers the population which might be affected by a risk; ie the number of people who might be exposed and the consequences for them.

Risk therefore reflects both the likelihood that harm will occur and its severity.

6   In some cases, this detailed approach may not be necessary since all the hazards are known and the risks are readily apparent and can therefore be addressed directly.

Purpose of risk assessment in this Regulation

7   The purpose of the risk assessment is to help the employer or self-employed person to determine what measures should be taken to comply with the employer's or self-employed person's duties under the "relevant statutory provisions". This phrase covers the general duties in the Health and Safety at Work etc Act 1974 and the more specific duties in the various Acts and Regulations (including these Regulations) associated with the HSW Act.

8   Regulation 3 does not itself stipulate the measures to be taken as a result of the risk assessment. The measures in each workplace will derive from compliance with other health and safety duties as described above, taking carefully into account the risk assessment. In essence, the risk assessment guides the judgement of the employer or the self-employed person, as to the measures they ought to take to fulfil their statutory obligations.

Suitable and sufficient

9   A suitable and sufficient risk assessment:

(a)   should identify the significant risks arising out of work.

     This means focussing on those risks that are liable to arise because of the work activity.

     Trivial risks can usually be ignored as can risks arising from routine activities associated with life in general, unless the work activity compounds those risks, or there is evidence of significant relevance to the particular work activity.

Employers and the self-employed are expected to take reasonable steps, eg by reading HSE guidance, the trade press, company or supplier manuals etc to familiarise themselves with the hazards and risks in their work.

(b) should enable the employer or the self-employed person to identify and prioritise the measures that need to be taken to comply with the relevant statutory provisions.

(c) should be appropriate to the nature of the work and such that it remains valid for a reasonable period of time.

This will enable the risk assessment and the significant findings to be used positively by management, eg to change working procedures or to introduce medium to long-term controls.

For relatively static operations, the risk assessment should be such that it is not necessary to repeat it every time someone is exposed to a hazard in comparable circumstances.

For more dynamic activities, ie where the detailed work activity may change fairly frequently or the workplace itself changes and develops (eg on a temporary work site[1] or where the work involves peripatetic workers moving from site to site) the risk assessment might have to concentrate more on the broad range of risks that might arise so that detailed planning and employee training can take account of those risks and enable them to be controlled as and when they arise.

Review and revision

10 The Regulation requires employers and the self-employed to review and, if necessary, modify their risk assessments, since assessment should not be a once-and-for-all activity. The nature of work changes; the appreciation of hazards and risks may develop. Monitoring under the arrangements required by Regulation 4 may reveal near misses or defects in plant. Adverse events may take place even if a suitable and sufficient risk assessment has been made and appropriate preventive and protective measures taken.

11 The employer or self-employed person needs to review the risk assessment if there are developments that suggest that it may no longer be valid (or that it can be improved). In most cases, it is prudent to plan to review risk assessments at regular intervals - the time between reviews being dependent on the nature of the risks and the degree of change likely in the work activity. Such reviews should form part of standard management practice.

Risk assessment in practice

12 There are no fixed rules about how a risk assessment should be undertaken, although paragraph 16 sets out the general principles that should be followed. The assessment will depend on the nature of the undertaking and the type and extent of the hazards and risks. Above all the process needs to be practical and it should involve management, whether or not advisers or consultants assist with the detail. Employers should ensure that those involved take all reasonable care in carrying out the risk assessment although the assessment would not be expected to cover risks which were not reasonably foreseeable.

[1] Such as a construction site

13   For small undertakings presenting few or simple hazards a suitable and sufficient risk assessment can be a very straightforward process based on judgement and requiring no specialist skills or complicated techniques. At the other extreme, in the case of, for example, complex chemical, large scale mineral extraction, or nuclear plant, it may need to be developed so far as to produce the basis for a complete safety case or report for the plant incorporating such techniques as quantified risk assessment.

14   In many intermediate cases it will not be possible to make a suitable and sufficient assessment without specialist advice in respect of unfamiliar risks, such as those requiring some knowledge of ergonomics or the more complex processes and techniques in the enterprise. And some risks cannot be properly evaluated without the application of modern techniques of measurement.

15   In some cases a single exercise covering all risks in a workplace or activity may be appropriate; in other cases separate assessment exercises for the risks arising from particular operations or groups of hazards may be more effective. But in all cases, it is important that the employer or self-employed person adopts a structured approach to risk assessment.

16   In particular a risk assessment should:

(a)   ensure that all relevant risks or hazards are addressed;

    (i)   the aim is to identify the significant risks in the workplace. Do not obscure those risks with an excess of information or by concentrating on trivial risks;

    (ii)   in most cases, first identify the hazards, ie those aspects of work (eg substances or equipment used, work processes or work organisation) which have the potential to cause harm;

    (iii)   if there are specific Acts or Regulations to be complied with, these may help to identify the hazards;

    (iv)   assess the risks from the identified hazards; if there are no hazards, there are no risks. Some risks may already be controlled in some way, whether by deliberate measures or by the circumstances in which they are found. The effectiveness of those controls needs to be taken into account in assessing the residual risk;

    (v)   be systematic in looking at hazards and risks. For example it may be necessary to look at hazards or risks in groups such as machinery, transport, substances, electrical etc. In other cases, an operation by operation approach may be needed, eg materials in production, dispatch, offices etc;

    (vi)   ensure all aspects of the work activity are reviewed.

(b)   address what actually happens in the workplace or during the work activity;

    (i)   actual practice may differ from the works manual; indeed this is frequently a route whereby risks creep in unnoticed;

    (ii)   think about the non-routine operations, eg maintenance operations, loading and unloading, changes in production cycles;

(iii) interruptions to the work activity are a frequent cause of accidents. Look at management of such incidents and the procedures to be followed;

(c) ensure that all groups of employees and others who might be affected are considered;

do not forget office staff, night cleaners, maintenance staff, security guards, visitors;

(d) identify groups of workers who might be particularly at risk;

for example young or inexperienced workers; those who work alone; any disabled staff;

(e) take account of existing preventive or precautionary measures;

they may already reduce the risk sufficiently in terms of what needs to be done to comply with relevant statutory provisions. *But* are they working properly? Does action need to be taken to ensure they are properly maintained?

17 The level of detail in a risk assessment should be broadly proportionate to the risk. The purpose is not to catalogue every trivial hazard; nor is the employer or self-employed person expected to be able to anticipate hazards beyond the limits of current knowledge. A suitable and sufficient risk assessment will reflect what it is reasonably practicable to expect employers to know about the hazards in their workplaces.

18 Where employees of different employers work in the same workplace their respective employers would have to consider risks to their own employees and to the other employer's employees and may have to co-operate to produce an overall risk assessment. Detailed requirements on co-operation and co-ordination are covered by Regulation 9.

19 In some cases employers may make a first rough assessment, to eliminate from consideration those risks on which no further action need be taken. This should also show where a fuller assessment is needed, if appropriate, using more sophisticated techniques. However, care should be taken not to exaggerate the level of sophistication needed. As mentioned above, the use of quantified risk assessment will be needed only in the most extreme cases, and most of those are already identified by specific Regulations.

20 Employers who control a number of similar workplaces containing similar activities may produce a basic 'model' risk assessment reflecting the core hazards and risks associated with these activities. 'Model' assessments may also be developed by trade associations, employers' bodies or other organisations concerned with a particular activity. Such 'model' assessments may be applied by employers or managers at each workplace, but only if they:

(a) satisfy themselves that the 'model' assessment is broadly appropriate to their type of work; and

(b) adapt the 'model' to the detail of their own actual work situations, including any extension necessary to cover hazards and risks not referred to in the 'model'.

Assessment under other Regulations

21   Other Regulations also contain requirements for risk assessment but which are addressed specifically to the hazards and risks that are covered by those Regulations. An assessment made for the purpose of such Regulations will cover in part the obligation to make assessments under these Regulations. Where employers have already carried out assessments under other Regulations, they need not repeat those assessments so long as they remain valid; but they do need to ensure that all significant risks are covered.

22   Where an employer is assessing a work situation or activity for the first time, a first rough assessment may be particularly useful in identifying those aspects of the work where a more detailed risk assessment may be needed in accordance with other Regulations. The overall risk assessment under this Regulation might then consist of separate risk assessments covering particular duties under other Regulations plus a further risk assessment covering any aspects of the work not covered elsewhere.

Recording

23   While all employers and self-employed persons are required to make a risk assessment, the Regulation also provides that employers with five or more employees must record the significant findings of their risk assessment. This record should represent an effective statement of hazards and risks which then leads management to take the relevant actions to protect health and safety. It needs therefore to be a part of an employer's overall approach to health and safety and where appropriate should be linked to other health and safety records or documents such as the record of health and safety arrangements required by Regulation 4 and the written health and safety policy statement required by Section 2(3) of the Health and Safety at Work Act.

24   This record would normally be in writing; however, it could also be recorded by other means, eg electronically, so long as it is retrievable for use by management or for examination, eg by an inspector or a safety representative. The record will often refer to and rely on other documents and records describing procedures and safeguards. In cases of highly hazardous plant which is required by law to present a 'safety case', the safety case documents will frequently incorporate the risk assessment so far as the main processes are concerned, and will probably be referred to as an ancillary document.

25   The significant findings should include:

(a)   the significant hazards identified in the assessment. That is, those hazards which might pose serious risk to workers or others who might be affected by the work activity if they were not properly controlled;

(b)   the existing control measures in place and the extent to which they control the risks (this need not replicate details of measures more fully described in works manuals etc but could refer to them);

(c)   the population which may be affected by these significant risks or hazards, including any groups of employees who are especially at risk.

26   In many cases, employers (or the self-employed) will need to record sufficient detail of the assessment itself, in addition to the significant findings, so that they can demonstrate (eg to an inspector or to safety representatives) that they have undertaken a suitable and sufficient assessment and also so that if circumstances change the assessment can be readily reviewed and, if

necessary, revised. Only in the most straightforward and obvious cases in which the risk assessment can be easily repeated and explained is a record totally unnecessary.

Preventive and protective measures

27   The preventive and protective measures that have to be taken following the risk assessment depend upon the relevant legislation - both the Health and Safety at Work Act and legislation covering particular hazards or sectors of work - and the risk assessment. In deciding upon the measures employers and self-employed should apply the following principles:

(a)   it is always best *if possible to avoid a risk altogether*, eg by not using or stocking a particular dangerous substance or article if it is not essential to the business;

(b)   *combat risks at source*, rather than by palliative measures. Thus, if the steps are slippery, treating or replacing them is better than providing a warning sign;

(c)   *wherever possible, adapt work to the individual* especially as regards the design of workplaces, the choice of work equipment and the choice of working and production methods, with a view in particular to alleviating monotonous work and work at a predetermined work rate. This helps reduce possible adverse effects on health and safety;

(d)   *take advantage of technological and technical progress,*which often offers opportunities for improving working methods and making them safer;

(e)   risk prevention measures need to *form part of a coherent policy and approach* having the effect of progressively reducing those risks that cannot be prevented or avoided altogether, and which will take account of the way work is to be organised, working conditions, the working environment and any relevant social factors. Health and safety policies required under Section 2(3) of the Health and Safety at Work Act should be prepared and applied by reference to these principles;

(f)   *give a priority to those measures which protect the whole workplace* and all those who work there, and so yield the greatest benefit; ie give collective protective measures priority over individual measures;

(g)   workers, whether employees or self-employed *need to understand what they need to do*;

(h)   the avoidance, prevention and reduction of risks at work needs to be an accepted part of the approach and attitudes at all levels of the organisation and to apply to all its activities, *ie the existence of an active health and safety culture affecting the organisation as a whole needs to be assured.*

Health and safety arrangements

(1) Every employer shall make and give effect to such arrangements as are appropriate, having regard to the nature of his activities and the size of his undertaking, for the effective planning, organisation, control, monitoring and review of the preventive and protective measures.

(2) Where the employer employs five or more employees, he shall record the arrangements referred to in paragraph (1).

28 This Regulation in effect requires employers to have arrangements in place to cover health and safety. It should be integrated with the management system for all other purposes. The system in place will depend on the size and nature of the activities of the undertaking but generally will include the following elements which are typical of any other management function:

(a) *Planning*: Adopting a systematic approach which identifies priorities and sets objectives. Whenever possible, risks are eliminated by the careful selection and design of facilities, equipment and processes or minimised by the use of physical control measures.

(b) *Organisation*: Putting in place the necessary structure with the aim of ensuring that there is a progressive improvement in health and safety performance.

(c) *Control*: Ensuring that the decisions for ensuring and promoting health and safety are being implemented as planned.

(d) *Monitoring and review*: Like quality, progressive improvement in health and safety can only be achieved through the constant development of policies, approaches to implementation and techniques of risk control.

29 The Regulation also provides that undertakings with five or more employees should record their arrangements for health and safety. The arrangements recorded should include a list of those competent persons appointed under Regulation 6. As with the risk assessment, this record could form part of the same document containing the health and safety policy required under Section 2(3) of the Health and Safety at Work Act.

Health surveillance

Every employer shall ensure that his employees are provided with such health surveillance as is appropriate having regard to the risks to their health and safety which are identified by the assessment.

30 The risk assessment will identify circumstances in which health surveillance is required by specific health and safety regulations (eg COSHH, Asbestos). In addition, health surveillance should be introduced where the assessment shows the following criteria to apply:

(a) there is an identifiable disease or adverse health condition related to the work concerned;

(b) valid techniques are available to detect indications of the disease or condition;

(c) there is a reasonable likelihood that the disease or condition may occur under the particular conditions of work; and (d)　surveillance is likely to further the protection of the health of the employees to be covered.

31　The primary benefit, and therefore the objective, of health surveillance should be to detect adverse health effects at an early stage, thereby enabling further harm to be prevented. In addition the results of health surveillance can provide a means of:

(a)　checking the effectiveness of control measures;

(b)　providing feedback on the accuracy of the risk assessment;

(c)　identifying and protecting individuals at increased risk.

32　Once it is decided that health surveillance is appropriate, such health surveillance should be maintained during the employee's employment unless the risk to which the worker is exposed and associated health effects are short term. The minimum requirement for health surveillance is the keeping of an individual health record. Where it is appropriate, health surveillance may also involve one or more health surveillance procedures depending on their suitability in the circumstances. Such procedures can include:

(a)　inspection of readily detectable conditions by a responsible person acting within the limits of their training and experience;

(b)　enquiries about symptoms, inspection and examination by a qualified person such as an Occupational Health Nurse;

(c)　medical surveillance, which may include clinical examination and measurements of physiological or psychological effects by an appropriately qualified practitioner;

(d)　biological effect monitoring, ie the measurement and assessment of early biological effects such as diminished lung function in exposed workers;

(e)　biological monitoring, ie the measurement and assessment of workplace agents or their metabolites either in tissues, secreta, excreta, expired air or any combination of these in exposed workers.

33　The frequency of the use of such methods should be determined either on the basis of suitable general guidance (eg as regards skin inspection for dermal effects) or on the advice of a qualified practitioner; the employees concerned should be given an opportunity to comment on the proposed frequency of such health surveillance procedures and should have access to an appropriately qualified practitioner for advice on surveillance.

Health and safety assistance

(1)　Every employer shall, subject to paragraphs (6) and (7), appoint one or more competent persons to assist him in undertaking the measures he needs to take to comply with the requirements and prohibitions imposed upon him by or under the relevant statutory provisions.

(2)　Where an employer appoints persons in accordance with paragraph (1), he shall make arrangements for ensuring adequate co-operation between them.

(3)   The employer shall ensure that the number of persons appointed under paragraph (1), the time available for them to fulfil their functions and the means at their disposal are adequate having regard to the size of his undertaking, the risks to which his employees are exposed and the distribution of those risks throughout the undertaking.

(4)   The employer shall ensure that -

(a)   any person appointed by him in accordance with paragraph(1) who is not in his employment -

> *(i)   is informed of the factors known by him to affect, or suspected by him of affecting, the health and safety of any other person who may be affected by the conduct of his undertaking, and*

> *(ii)   has access to the information referred to in regulation 8; and*

(b)   any person appointed by him in accordance with paragraph(1) is given such information about any person working in his undertaking who is -

> *(i)   employed by him under a fixed-term contract of employment, or*

> *(ii)   employed in an employment business,*

> *as is necessary to enable that person properly to carry out the function specified in that paragraph.*

(5)   A person shall be regarded as competent for the purposes of paragraph (1) where he has sufficient training and experience or knowledge and other qualities to enable him properly to assist in undertaking the measures referred to in that paragraph.

(6)   Paragraph (1) shall not apply to a self-employed employer who is not in partnership with any other person where he has sufficient training and experience or knowledge and other qualities properly to undertake the measures referred to in that paragraph himself.

(7)   Paragraph (1) shall not apply to individuals who are employers and who are together carrying on business in partnership where at least one of the individuals concerned has sufficient training and experience or knowledge and other qualities -

(a)   properly to undertake the measures he needs to take to comply with the requirements and prohibitions imposed upon him by or under the relevant statutory provisions; and

(b)   properly to assist his fellow partners in undertaking the measures they need to take to comply with the requirements and prohibitions imposed upon them by or under the relevant statutory provisions.

34   Employers must have access to competent help in applying the provisions of health and safety law, including these Regulations and in particular in devising and applying protective measures unless they are competent to undertake the measures without assistance. Appointment of competent persons for this purpose should be included among the arrangements recorded under Regulation 4(2).

35 Employers may appoint one or more of their own employees to do all that is necessary or may enlist help or support from outside the organisation, or they may do both. Employers who are sole traders, or are members of partnerships, may appoint themselves (or other partners) to carry out health and safety measures, so long as they are competent. Large employers may well appoint a whole department with specific health and safety responsibilities including specialists in such matters as occupational hygiene or safety engineering. In any case where external support is brought in, its activities must be co-ordinated by those appointed by the employer to manage the health and safety measures.

36 External services employed usually will be appointed in an advisory capacity only. They will often be specialists or general consultants on health and safety matters.

37 The appointment of such health and safety assistants, departments or advisers does not absolve the employer from responsibilities for health and safety under the Health and Safety at Work Act and other relevant statutory provisions. It can do no more than give added assurance that these responsibilities will be discharged adequately.

38 Employers are solely responsible for ensuring that those they appoint to assist them with health and safety measures are competent to carry out whatever tasks they are assigned and given adequate information and support. In making their decisions employers should take into account the need for:

(a)   a knowledge and understanding of the work involved, the principles of risk assessment and prevention, and current health and safety applications;

(b)   the capacity to apply this to the task required by the employer which might include identifying the health and safety problems, assessing the need for action, designing and developing strategy and plans, implementing these strategies and plans, evaluating their effectiveness and promoting and communicating health and safety and welfare advances and practices.

39 Competence in the sense it is used in these Regulations does not necessarily depend on the possession of particular skills or qualifications. Simple situations may require only the following:

(a)   an understanding of relevant current best practice;

(b)   awareness of the limitations of one's own experience and knowledge; and

(c)   the willingness and ability to supplement existing experience and knowledge.

40 The provision of effective health and safety measures in more complex or highly technical situations will call for specific applied knowledge and skills which can be offered by appropriately qualified specialists. In the case of specific knowledge and skills in occupational health and safety, membership of a professional body or similar organisation at an appropriate level and in an appropriate part of health and safety, or possession of an appropriate qualification in health and safety, can help to guide employers. Competence based qualifications accredited by the National Council for Vocational Qualifications and SCOTVEC (the Scottish Vocational Education Council), which are being developed for most occupations, may also provide a guide.

Procedures for serious and imminent danger and for danger areas

(1) Every employer shall -

(a) establish and where necessary give effect to appropriate procedures to be followed in the event of serious and imminent danger to persons at work in his undertaking;

(b) nominate a sufficient number of competent persons to implement those procedures insofar as they relate to the evacuation from premises of persons at work in his undertaking; and

(c) ensure that none of his employees has access to any area occupied by him to which it is necessary to restrict access on grounds of health and safety unless the employee concerned has received adequate health and safety instruction.

(2) Without prejudice to the generality of paragraph(1)(a), the procedures referred to in that sub-paragraph shall -

(a) so far as is practicable, require any persons at work who are exposed to serious and imminent danger to be informed of the nature of the hazard and of the steps taken or to be taken to protect them from it;

(b) enable the persons concerned (if necessary by taking appropriate steps in the absence of guidance or instruction and in the light of their knowledge and the technical means at their disposal) to stop work and immediately proceed to a place of safety in the event of their being exposed to serious, imminent and unavoidable danger; and

(c) save in exceptional cases for reasons duly substantiated (which cases and reasons shall be specified in those procedures), require the persons concerned to be prevented from resuming work in any situation where there is still a serious and imminent danger.

(3) A person shall be regarded as competent for the purposes of paragraph(1)(b) where he has sufficient training and experience or knowledge and other qualities to enable him properly to implement the evacuation procedures referred to in that sub-paragraph.

41   Employers need to establish procedures to be followed by any worker if situations presenting serious and imminent danger were to arise. The aim has to be to set out clear guidance on when employees and others at work should stop work and how they should move to a place of safety. In some cases this will require full evacuation of the workplace. In other cases it might mean some or all of the workforce moving to a safer part of the workplace.

42   The risk assessment should identify the foreseeable events that need to be covered by these procedures. For some employers, fire (and possibly bomb) risks will be the only ones that need to be covered. But even in those cases the nature of the fire risk (eg in which parts of a building, the substances that might be involved etc) may need to be reflected in the detail of the procedures.

43   Many workplaces or work activities will pose additional risks. All employers should consider carefully in their risk assessment whether such additional risks might arise. Where such risks are identified, additional procedures will be needed and those procedures should be geared, as far as is

13

practicable, to the nature of the serious and imminent danger that those risks might pose.

44 The procedures may need to take account of responsibilities of specific employees. Some employees, or groups of employees, may have specific tasks to perform in the event of emergencies (eg to shut down plant that might otherwise compound the danger); some employees may have had training so that they can seek to bring an emergency event under control. The circumstances in which such workers should stop work and move to a place of safety may well be different from those for other workers; the procedures should if necessary reflect these differences.

45 The procedures should set out the role and responsibilities of the competent persons nominated to implement the detailed actions. The procedures should also ensure that employees know who the relevant competent persons are and understand their role.

46 Some specific emergency situations will be covered by certain health and safety regulations. Employers' procedures should reflect any requirements laid on them by such regulations.

47 Procedures should cater for the fact that emergency events can occur and develop rapidly, thus requiring employees to act without waiting for further guidance. The procedures should specify when and how they are to be activated so that employees can proceed in good time to a place of safety. For example, it may be necessary to commence evacuation while attempts to control an emergency (eg a process in danger of running out of control) are still under way, in case those attempts fail.

48 Emergency procedures should normally be written down (eg under Regulation 4(2)), clearly setting out the limits of actions to be taken by employees. Information on the procedures should be made available to all employees (under Regulation 8), to any external health and safety personnel appointed under Regulation 6(1), and, if necessary, to other workers and/or their employers under Regulation 10. They should also form part of induction training under Regulation 11. It may be advisable to carry out exercises to familiarise employees with the procedures (eg the use of alarms etc to initiate action) and to test their effectiveness.

49 Work should not be resumed after an emergency if a serious danger remains. If there are any doubts expert assistance should be sought, eg from the emergency services and others. The occurrence of an emergency may also indicate the need for a review of the risk assessment (paragraphs 8-9). There may, for certain groups of workers, be exceptional circumstances when re-entry to areas of serious danger may be deemed necessary, eg the emergency services where human life is at risk. Where such exceptional circumstances can be anticipated, the procedures should set out the special protective measures to be taken (and the pre-training required) and the steps to be taken for authorisation of such actions.

50 Where different employers (or self-employed persons) share a workplace their separate emergency procedures should take account of others in the workplace and as far as is appropriate should be co-ordinated. Detailed requirements on co-operation and co-ordination are covered by Regulation 9.

Danger areas

51 A danger area is a work environment which must be entered by an employee where the level of risk is unacceptable without special precautions

being taken. Such areas are not necessarily static in that minor alterations or an emergency may convert a normal work environment into a danger area. The hazard involved need not occupy the whole area, such as a toxic gas, but can be localised where an employee is likely to come into contact, such as bare live electrical conductors. The area must be restricted to prevent inadvertent access by other employees and other persons.

52   This Regulation does not specify the precautions that should be taken to ensure safe working in the danger area - this is covered by other legislation. However, once the employer has established suitable precautions the relevant employees must receive adequate instruction in those precautions prior to entry into any such danger area.

Information for employees

Every employer shall provide his employees with comprehensible and relevant information on -

(a)   *the risks to their health and safety identified by the assessment;*

(b)   *the preventive and protective measures;*

(c)   *the procedures referred to in regulation 7(1)(a);*

(d)   *the identity of those persons nominated by him in accordance with regulation 7(1)(b); and*

(e)   *the risks notified to him in accordance with regulation 9(1)(c).*

53   The risk assessment will help identify information which has to be provided to employees under specific regulations, as well as any further information relevant to risks to employees' health and safety. Relevant information on risks and on preventive and protective measures will be limited to what employees need to know to ensure their health and safety. The Regulation also requires information to be provided on the emergency arrangements established under Regulation 7, including the identity of staff nominated to assist in the event of evacuation.

54   To be comprehensible, information must be capable of being understood by the employees to whom it is addressed. This should take account of their level of training, knowledge and experience. Special consideration should be given to any employees with language difficulties or with disabilities which may impede their receipt of information. For employees with little or no understanding of English or who cannot read English, employers may need to make special arrangements. These could include providing translation, using interpreters, or in some cases replacing written notices with clearly understood symbols or diagrams.

55   Information can be provided in whatever form is most suitable in the circumstances, so long as it is comprehensible.

56   This Regulation applies to all employees, including trainees and those on fixed-duration contracts. Additional information requirements for employees on fixed-duration contracts are contained in Regulation 13.

Co-operation and co-ordination

(1)   Where two or more employers share a workplace (whether on a temporary or a permanent basis) each such employer shall -

(a)   co-operate with the other employers concerned so far as is necessary to enable them to comply with the requirements and prohibitions imposed upon them by or under the relevant statutory provisions;

(b)   (taking into account the nature of his activities) take all reasonable steps to co-ordinate the measures he takes to comply with the requirements and prohibitions imposed upon him by or under the relevant statutory provisions with the measures the other employers concerned are taking to comply with the requirements and prohibitions imposed upon them by or under the relevant statutory provisions; and

(c)   take all reasonable steps to inform the other employers concerned of the risks to their employees' health and safety arising out of or in connection with the conduct by him of his undertaking.

(2)   Paragraph(1) shall apply to employers sharing a workplace with self-employed persons and to self-employed persons sharing a workplace with other self-employed persons as it applies to employers sharing a workplace with other employers; and the references in that paragraph to employers and the reference in the said paragraph to their employees shall be construed accordingly.

57   Employers and the self-employed have obligations under the Health and Safety at Work Act towards anyone who may be put at risk by their activities. Where the activities of different employers and self-employed people interact, for example where they share premises or workplaces, they may need to co-operate with each other to ensure that their respective obligations are met. This Regulation makes specific the duty to co-operate where employers and the self-employed share a workplace, ie where they have a physical presence on the same worksite.

58   The duties to co-operate and to co-ordinate measures relate to all statutory duties and therefore concern all people who may be at risk, both on and off-site. The specific duty to exchange information relates only to those employees and the self-employed who are at risk on-site, though co-operation on off-site risks may also involve exchanging information. A self-employed contractor carrying out work on an employer's or self-employed person's premises would be regarded as sharing the workplace for the purposes of Regulation 9.

59   Risk assessments under Regulation 3 and subsequent measures (in particular emergency procedures under Regulation 7) may need to cover the workplace as a whole to be fully effective, which will require some degree of co-ordination. The form of co-ordination adopted will depend on the circumstances, but all employers and self-employed involved will need to satisfy themselves that the arrangements adopted are adequate. Employers will also need to ensure that all their employees, but especially the competent persons appointed under Regulations 6 and 7, are aware of and take full part in the arrangements. In some cases, specific co-ordination arrangements will be required by other regulations[2].

---

[2] For example, under regulations which are likely to be made to implement the Temporary and Mobile Construction Sites Directive.

60   Where a particular employer (eg the main employer) controls the worksite, other employers or self-employed sharing the site should assist the controlling employer in assessing the shared risks and co-ordinating any necessary measures, primarily by providing information. A controlling employer who has established site-wide arrangements will have to inform new minor employers or self-employed so that they can integrate themselves into the arrangements.

Appointment of health and safety co-ordinator

61   Where there is no controlling employer, the employers and self-employed persons present should agree such joint arrangements, such as appointing a health and safety co-ordinator, as are needed to meet the Regulations' requirements. In workplaces where management control is fragmented and employment is largely casual or short-term[3], appointing a health and safety supervisor or co-ordinator is likely to be the most effective way of ensuring co-ordination and co-operation and the efficient exchange of information. The co-ordinator would be responsible for bringing together the efforts of individual employers and self-employed persons across the workplace. In worksites which are complex or contain significant hazards, the controlling employer or health and safety co-ordinator (on behalf of the employers etc present) may need to seek competent advice in making or assisting with the risk assessment and determining appropriate measures.

Persons in control

62   Even when the person in control of a multi-occupancy workplace is not an employer of persons working in that workplace or self-employed, such persons will nonetheless need to co-operate with those occupying the workplace under their control; for example, procedures for authorising or carrying out repairs and modifications will have to take account of the need for co-operation and exchanges of information. Such co-operation will be needed to carry out effectively the general duties placed on such persons under Section 4 of the Health and Safety at Work Act as well as as more specific duties under certain regulations (eg in offshore health and safety legislation or in relation to welfare facilities provided under the Workplace (Health, Safety and Welfare) Regulations 1992).

63   Where the circumstances in paragraph 59 apply, and there is also a person (who is not an employer on those premises or self-employed) in control of the workplace, then the joint arrangements (including, if appropriate, the appointment of a health and safety co-ordinator) will need to be agreed with that person, as well as the employers (or self-employed) present.

64   Where any persons in control of premises make arrangements to co-ordinate health and safety activities, particularly for emergencies, this may be sufficient to enable employers and the self-employed who participate in those arrangements to comply with Regulation 9(1)(b).

65   This Regulation does not apply to multi-occupancy buildings or sites where each unit under the control of an individual tenant employer or self-employed person will be regarded as a separate workplace. In some cases, however, the common parts of such multi-occupancy sites may be shared workplaces (eg a common reception area in an office building) or may be under the control of a person to whom Section 4 of the HSW Act applies (see paragraph 60 above) and suitable arrangements may need to be put in place to cover these areas, including the appointment of a health and safety co-ordinator where appropriate.

[3] In construction, for example.

Persons working in host employers' or self-employed persons' undertakings

(1)   Every employer and every self-employed person shall ensure that the employer of any employees from an outside undertaking who are working in his undertaking is provided with comprehensible information on -

(a)   the risks to those employees' health and safety arising out of or in connection with the conduct by that first-mentioned employer or by that self-employed person of his undertaking; and

(b)   the measures taken by that first-mentioned employer or by that self-employed person in compliance with the requirements and prohibitions imposed upon him by or under the relevant statutory provisions insofar as the said requirements and prohibitions relate to those employees.

(2)   Paragraph (1) shall apply to a self-employed person who is working in the undertaking of an employer or a self-employed person as it applies to employees from an outside undertaking who are working therein; and the reference in that paragraph to the employer of any employees from an outside undertaking who are working in the undertaking of an employer or a self-employed person and the references in the said paragraph to employees from an outside undertaking who are working in the undertaking of an employer or a self-employed person shall be construed accordingly.

(3)   Every employer shall ensure that any person working in his undertaking who is not his employee and every self-employed person (not being an employer) shall ensure that any person working in his undertaking is provided with appropriate instructions and comprehensible information regarding any risks to that person's health and safety which arise out of the conduct by that employer or self-employed person of his undertaking.

(4)   Every employer shall -

(a)   ensure that the employer of any employees from an outside undertaking who are working in his undertaking is provided with sufficient information to enable that second-mentioned employer to identify any person nominated by that first-mentioned employer in accordance with regulation 7(1)(b) to implement evacuation procedures as far as those employees are concerned; and

(b)   take all reasonable steps to ensure that any employees from an outside undertaking who are working in his undertaking receive sufficient information to enable them to identify any person nominated by him in accordance with regulation 7(1)(b) to implement evacuation procedures as far as they are concerned.

(5)   Paragraph (4) shall apply to a self-employed person who is working in an employer's undertaking as it applies to employees from an outside undertaking who are working therein; and the reference in that paragraph to the employer of any employees from an outside undertaking who are working in an employer's undertaking and the references in the said paragraph to employees from an outside undertaking who are working in an employer's undertaking shall be construed accordingly.

66   This Regulation applies where employees or self-employed persons carry out work in the undertaking (or business) of an employer other than their own or of another self-employed person. There will be some overlap with

18

Regulation 9 (mainly in the case of some self-employed contractors), for which adequate arrangements established under Regulation 9 should suffice. However, this Regulation does not depend on workplaces being shared. Employers and the self-employed who are sole occupiers may also need to provide comprehensible information to other employers whose employees (or to other self-employed) carry out work, often for a short time, on behalf of the first employers or self-employed, at any place. Such employees would include:

(a) contractors' employees carrying out cleaning, repair, or maintenance under a service contract;

(b) employees in temporary employment businesses hired to work under the first employer's control (additional requirements for information to employment businesses are under Regulation 13).

67 The risk assessment under Regulation 3 will have identified risks to these people. The information provided must include those risks and the health and safety measures in place to address those risks and be sufficient to enable the other employers to identify any persons that they (the first employer) have nominated to help with emergency evacuation. The first employer also has a duty to take reasonable steps to ensure that the employees of the second employer have indeed received the latter information.

68 People who visit another employer's premises to carry out work must be provided with appropriate information and instructions regarding relevant risks to their health and safety. These visitors could be specialists who are better informed than the host employer of the risks normally associated with the tasks which they are to carry out. The host employer's instructions should be concerned with those risks which are peculiar to his activity or premises. The visitors may also introduce risks to the permanent workforce (eg from equipment or substances they may bring with them). Their employers should inform the host employer of such risks, under their general duty under Section 3 of the Health and Safety at Work Act. The risk assessment under Regulation 3(1)(b) should identify the necessary information.

69 The guidance on comprehensibility of information under Regulation 8 (paragraphs 51-54 of this Code) applies equally to information provided under Regulation 10.

Capabilities and training

(1)   Every employer shall, in entrusting tasks to his employees, take into account their capabilities as regards health and safety.

(2)   Every employer shall ensure that his employees are provided with adequate health and safety training -

(a)   on their being recruited into the employer's undertaking; and

(b)   on their being exposed to new or increased risks because of -

(i)   their being transferred or given a change of responsibilities within the employer's undertaking,

(ii)   the introduction of new work equipment into or a change respecting work equipment already in use within the employer's undertaking,

(iii)   the introduction of new technology into the employer's undertaking, or

(iv)   the introduction of a new system of work into or a change respecting a system of work already in use within the employer's undertaking.

(3)   The training referred to in paragraph (2) shall -

(a)   be repeated periodically where appropriate;

(b)   be adapted to take account of any new or changed risks to the health and safety of the employees concerned; and

(c)   take place during working hours.

70   When allocating work to employees, employers should ensure that the demands of the job do not exceed the employees' ability to carry out the work without risk to themselves or others. Employers should take account of the employees' capabilities and the level of their training, knowledge and experience. If additional training is needed, it should be provided.

Training

71   Training is an important way of achieving competence and helps to convert information into safe working practices. It contributes to the organisation's health and safety culture and is needed at all levels, including top management. The risk assessment will help determine the level of training needed for each type of work as part of the preventive and protective measures. This can include basic skills training, specific on-the-job training and training in health and safety or emergency procedures.

72   Training needs are likely to be greatest on recruitment. New employees should receive basic induction training on health and safety, including arrangements for first-aid, fire and evacuation. Particular attention should be given to the needs of young workers. The risk assessment should indicate further specific training needs. In some cases, training may be required even though an employee already holds formal qualifications.

73   Changes in an employee's work environment may cause them to be exposed to new or increased risks, requiring further training. The need for further training should be considered when:

(a)   employees transfer or take on new responsibilities. There may be a change in the work activity or in the work environment;

(b)   there is a change in the work equipment or systems of work in use. A significant change is likely to need a review and re-assessment of risks, which may indicate additional training needs. If the change includes introducing completely new technology, it may bring with it new and unfamiliar risks. Competent outside advice may be needed.

Refresher training

74   An employee's competence will decline if skills (eg in emergency procedures) are not used regularly. Training therefore needs to be repeated periodically to ensure continued competence. Information from personal performance monitoring, health and safety checks, accident investigations and near miss incidents can help to establish a suitable period for re-training.

Special attention should be given to employees who occasionally deputise for others. Their skills are likely to be under-developed and they may need more frequent refresher training.

Adaptation/working hours

75   Changes in risks may also require changes in the content of training, eg where new procedures have been introduced. Health and safety training should take place during working hours. If it is necessary to arrange training outside an employee's normal hours, this should be treated as an extension of time at work.

Employees' duties

(1)   Every employee shall use any machinery, equipment, dangerous substance, transport equipment, means of production or safety device provided to him by his employer in accordance both with any training in the use of the equipment concerned which has been received by him and the instructions respecting that use which have been provided to him by the said employer in compliance with the requirements and prohibitions imposed upon that employer by or under the relevant statutory provisions.

(2)   Every employee shall inform his employer or any other employee of that employer with specific responsibility for the health and safety of his fellow employees -

(a)   of any work situation which a person with the first-mentioned employee's training and instruction would reasonably consider represented a serious and immediate danger to health and safety; and

(b)   of any matter which a person with the first-mentioned employee's training and instruction would reasonably consider represented a shortcoming in the employer's protection arrangements for health and safety,

insofar as that situation or matter either affects the health and safety of that first-mentioned employee or arises out of or in connection with his own activities at work, and has not previously been reported to his employer or to any other employee of that employer in accordance with this paragraph.

76   Employees have a duty under Section 7 of the Health and Safety at Work etc Act 1974 to take reasonable care for their own health and safety and of that of others who may be affected by their acts or omissions at work. Towards this end, employees should use correctly all work items provided by their employer, in accordance with their training and the instructions they receive to enable them to use the items safely.

77   Employees' duties under Section 7 also include co-operating with their employer to enable the employer to comply with statutory duties for health and safety. Employers or those they appoint (eg under Regulation 6) to assist them with health and safety matters therefore need to be informed without delay of any work situation which might present a serious and imminent danger. The danger could be to the employee concerned or, if it results from the employee's work, to others. Employees should also notify any shortcomings in the health and safety arrangements even when no immediate danger exists, so that employers in pursuit of their duties under the HSW Act and other statutory provisions can take such remedial action as may be needed.

78   The duties placed on employees do not reduce the responsibility of the employer to comply with duties under these Regulations and the other relevant statutory provisions. In particular, employers need to ensure that employees receive adequate instruction and training to enable them to comply with their duties under this Regulation.

Temporary workers

(1)   Every employer shall provide any person whom he has employed under a fixed-term contract of employment with comprehensible information on -

(a)   any special occupational qualifications or skills required to be held by that employee if he is to carry out his work safely; and

(b)   any health surveillance required to be provided to that employee by or under any of the relevant statutory provisions,

and shall provide the said information before the employee concerned commences his duties.

(2)   Every employer and every self-employed person shall provide any person employed in an employment business who is to carry out work in his undertaking with comprehensible information on -

(a)   any special occupational qualifications or skills required to be held by that employee if he is to carry out his work safely; and

(b)   any health surveillance required to be provided to that employee by or under any of the relevant statutory provisions.

(3)   Every employer and every self-employed person shall ensure that every person carrying on an employment business whose employees are to carry out work in his undertaking is provided with comprehensible information on -

(a)   any special occupational qualifications or skills required to be held by those employees if they are to carry out their work safely; and

(b)   the specific features of the jobs to be filled by those employees (insofar as those features are likely to affect their health and safety);

and the person carrying on the employment business concerned shall ensure that the information so provided is given to the said employees.

79   This Regulation supplements previous regulations requiring the provision of information with additional requirements on temporary workers (ie those employed on fixed-duration contracts and those employed in employment businesses, but working under the control of a user company). The use of temporary workers will also have been notified to health and safety personnel under Regulation 6(6), where necessary for the personnel to be able to carry out their functions.

Fixed-duration contracts

80   Regulation 8 deals with the provision of information by employers to their employees. This includes those on fixed-duration contracts. Under Regulation 13(1), employees on fixed-duration contracts also have to be informed of any special occupational qualifications or skills required to carry

out the work safely and whether the job is subject to statutory health surveillance (the latter being in any case a protective measure covered in general by Regulation 8(b)).

Employment businesses

81 Regulation 10(4) deals with the provision of information by employers to other employers whose employees are working in the first employer's undertaking. This includes employees of persons carrying on an employment business. Under Regulation 13(3), employment businesses also have to be informed of any special occupational qualifications or skills required to carry out the work safely and the specific features of the job which might affect health and safety (eg work at heights).

82 Both the person carrying on the employment business and the user employer have duties to provide information to the employee. The person carrying on the employment business has a duty under Regulation 8 (as an employer) and a duty under Regulation 13(3) to ensure that the information provided by the user employer is given to the employee. The user employer has a duty under Regulation 10(4) to check that information provided to an employer (including someone carrying on an employment business) is received by the employee. In addition, Regulations 13(1) and (2) require information on qualifications, skills and health surveillance to be provided directly to employees in an employment business.

83 These duties overlap to ensure that the information needs of those working for, but not employed by, user employers are not overlooked. User employers and persons carrying on employment businesses should therefore make suitable arrangements to satisfy themselves that information is provided. In most cases, it may be sufficient for information to be provided directly to employees by user employers, who will know the risks and preventive measures in their workplaces. Those carrying on employment businesses will need to satisfy themselves that arrangements for this are adequate. However, basic information on job demands and risks should be supplied to the employment business at an early stage to help select those most suitable to carry out the work (in accordance with Regulation 13(3)).

Self-employed

84 The self-employed have similar duties under Regulations 9(2) and 10 and Regulations 13(2) and 13(3) to inform employment businesses and the employees of employment businesses who carry out work in their undertakings. They may also need to agree arrangements with the employment businesses concerned. Self-employed workers hired through employment businesses are entitled to receive health and safety information from the employers or self-employed for whom they carry out work under Regulation 10(2).

Exemption certificates

(1)   The Secretary of State for Defence may, in the interests of national security, by a certificate in writing exempt -

(a)   any of the home forces, any visiting force or any headquarters from those requirements of these Regulations which impose obligations on employers; or

(b) any member of the home forces, any member of a visiting force or any member of a headquarters from the requirements imposed by regulation 12;

and any exemption such as is specified in sub-paragraph(a) or (b) of this paragraph may be granted subject to conditions and to a limit of time and may be revoked by the said Secretary of State by a further certificate in writing at any time.

(2)   In this regulation -

(a)   "the home forces" has the same meaning as in section 12(1) of the Visiting Forces Act 1952 [a];

(b)   "headquarters" has the same meaning as in article 3(2) of the Visiting Forces and International Headquarters (Application of Law) Order 1965 [b];

(c)   "member of a headquarters" has the same meaning as in paragraph 1(1) of the Schedule to the International Headquarters and Defence Organisations Act 1964 [c]; and

(d)   "visiting force" has the same meaning as it does for the purposes of any provision of Part I of the Visiting Forces Act 1952.

(a) 1952 c.67.
(b) S.I. 1965/1536, to which there are amendments not relevant to these Regulations.
(c) 1964 c.5.

Exclusion of civil liability

Breach of a duty imposed by these Regulations shall not confer a right of action in any civil proceedings.

Extension outside Great Britain

(1)   These Regulations shall, subject to regulation 2, apply to and in relation to the premises and activities outside Great Britain to which sections 1 to 59 and 80 to 82 of the Health and Safety at Work etc. Act 1974 apply by virtue of the Health and Safety at Work etc. Act 1974 (Application Outside Great Britain) Order 1989[d] as they apply within Great Britain.

(2)   For the purposes of Part I of the 1974 Act, the meaning of "at work" shall be extended so that an employee or a self-employed person shall be treated as being at work throughout the time that he is present at the premises to and in relation to which these Regulations apply by virtue of paragraph (1); and, in that connection, these Regulations shall have effect subject to the extension effected by this paragraph.

(d) S.I. 1989/840.

Modification of instrument

The Safety Representatives and Safety Committees Regulations 1977[e] shall be modified to the extent specified in the Schedule to these Regulations.

(e) S.I. 1977/500.

The following regulation shall be inserted after regulation 4 of the Safety Representatives and Safety Committees Regulations 1977 -

"Employer's duty to consult and provide facilities and assistance

4A. (1) Without prejudice to the generality of section 2(6) of the Health and Safety at Work etc. Act 1974, every employer shall consult safety representatives in good time with regard to -

    (a) the introduction of any measure at the workplace which may substantially affect the health and safety of the employees the safety representatives concerned represent;

    (b) his arrangements for appointing or, as the case may be, nominating persons in accordance with regulations 6(1) and 7(1)(b) of the Management of Health and Safety at Work Regulations 1992;

    (c) any health and safety information he is required to provide to the employees the safety representatives concerned represent by or under the relevant statutory provisions;

    (d) the planning and organisation of any health and safety training he is required to provide to the employees the safety representatives concerned represent by or under the relevant statutory provisions; and

    (e) the health and safety consequences for the employees the safety representatives concerned represent of the introduction (including the planning thereof) of new technologies into the workplace.

(2) Without prejudice to regulations 5 and 6 of these Regulations, every employer shall provide such facilities and assistance as safety representatives may reasonably require for the purpose of carrying out their functions under section 2(4) of the 1974 Act and under these Regulations.".

Printed in the United Kingdom for HSE, published by HMSO